They can't take that away fr

2

Oh, Lady be good

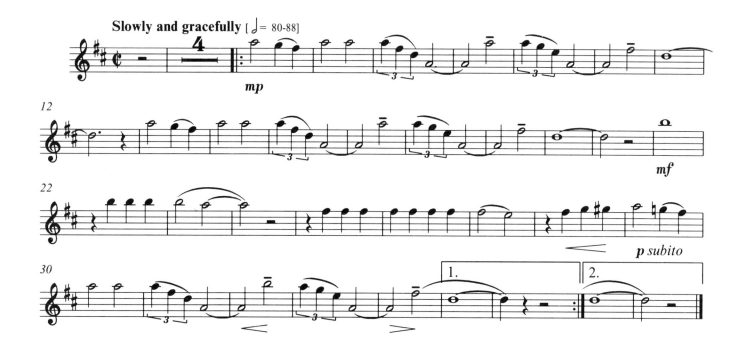

S'wonderful

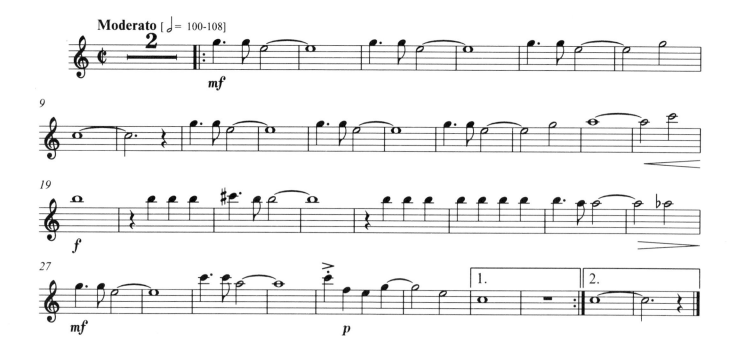

A foggy day

Embraceable you

4

Summertime

I got rhythm

It ain't necessarily so

Let's call the whole thing off

Bess, you is my woman now

Reproduced and printed by
Halstan & Co. Ltd., Amersham, Bucks., England

PLAY GERSHWIN

Solos for Bb and Eb instruments

(clarinet; trumpet; soprano, alto and tenor saxophone)

with piano accompaniment

from songs by

GEORGE GERSHWIN

(1896–1937)

arranged by Alan Gout

Faber Music Ltd

London

Contents

© 1988 by Faber Music Ltd
First published in 1988 by Faber Music Ltd
3 Queen Square, London WC1N 3AU
Music drawn by Barnes Music Engraving
Cover illustration © Brian Sweet
Cover typography by M & S Tucker
Printed in England by Halstan & Co Ltd

For copyright reasons, this edition is not for sale in the USA or Japan

They can't take that away from me

Oh, Lady be good

S'wonderful

A foggy day

Embraceable you

Summertime

I got rhythm

It ain't necessarily so

Let's call the whole thing off

Bess, you is my woman now

GREYSCALE

BIN TRAVELER FORM

Cut By *Manuel Orando*   Qty *40*   Date *12·5·24*

Scanned By_____ Qty_____Date_____

Scanned Batch IDs

_____ _____ _____

Notes / Exception

_____

_____

_____

_____

_____